Mel Bay Presents

Bluegrass & Country Music for Harmonica

DIATONIC • CROSS-HARP • CHROMATIC

By Phil Duncan

A stereo cassette tape of the music in this book is now available. The publisher strongly recommends the use of this cassette tape along with the text to insure accuracy of interpretation and ease in learning.

MUSICAL CONTENTS

DIATONIC HARMONICA

Each harmonica is designed in a certain "key". When using the harmonica in that stated "key" it is called standard or straight harmonica, such as the C harmonica is the key of C, the G harmonica is the key of G and the F harmonica is the key of F, etc. This also means that the center or "home" tone is the fourth hole of the diatonic harmonica. Each different key requires a different harmonica. You may be able to use any key harmonica in this book if you observe the numbers and arrows written below each musical line. Normally you would use the C harmonica for this book.

In playing straight harmonica, the method for blocking out unwanted tones is called "tongue blocking". Your tongue should cover and block off two or three undesired holes on the left of the harmonica mouth piece:

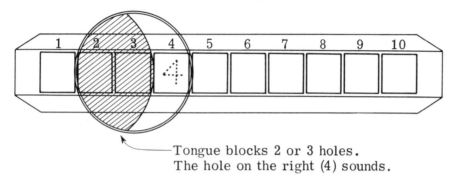

Tongue blocks 2 or 3 holes.
The hole on the right (4) sounds.

To be able to "chord" with melody, just release the tongue covered holes and a chord (3 or more tones together) will be produced.

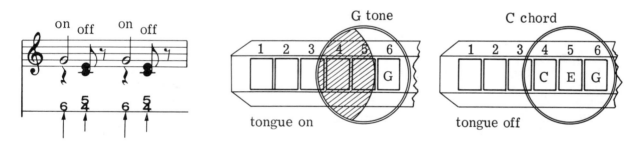

DIATONIC 10 HOLE NOTE CHART

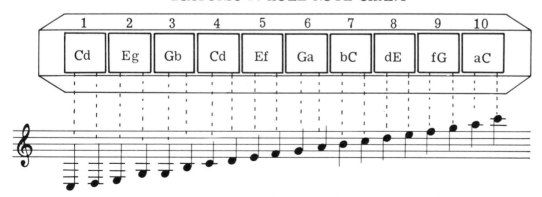

FOR FURTHER INFORMATION about the diatonic harmonica refer to:
Mel Bay's <u>DELUXE HARMONICA METHOD</u> by Phil Duncan.

CHROMATIC HARMONICA

The use of the slide button will give accurate half-step tones on the chromatic harmonica. The 12 or 16 hole chromatic harmonica have been notated in this book. A change of octaves becomes necessary for variety and ease of playing. (All octaves on the chromatic harmonica are the same, except the tones are higher or lower in pitch.)

EXAMPLE: same notational level

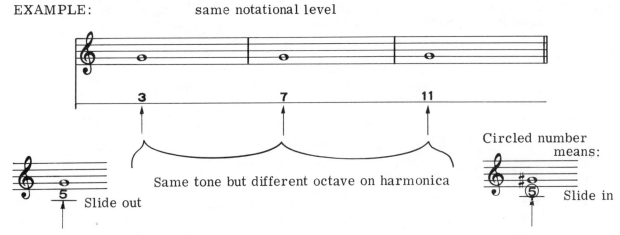

FOR FURTHER INFORMATION about chromatic harmonica refer to:
   Mel Bay's Complete CHROMATIC HARMONICA METHOD by
   Phil Duncan.

CROSS-HARP

The method for cross-harp is to cross over to hole 2 of the diatonic 10 hole harmonica and draw. This tone becomes (hole 2) the "key" center or "home" tone and changes the "key" in which the harmonica plays. Therefore, C harp plays cross-harp (blues harp) in the key of G. (G is the draw tone in hole 2) F harp plays cross-harp in the key of C. (C is a draw tone in hole 2 of the F harp) If the music is in the key of C use the F harmonica. The cross-harp technique allows for half step tones not normally played on the diatonic harmonica. All draw tones should begin below the pitch: <u>5</u> then rise quickly to pitch level.

To achieve the half steps or more, a blues technique called bending is used.
Notational information:

③ = half step   ③ = whole step down   ▽3 = whole step
   down   and a half

Octave changes need to take place for ease of playing. The numbers will dictate the changes:

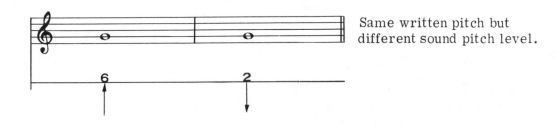

Same written pitch but different sound pitch level.

Notes in paranthesis are subsitute notes:

LIP BLOCKING is used to produce the single tone. This allows for greater pressure on the harmonica reeds. The harmonica player simply purses his lips so that only one sound can be made.

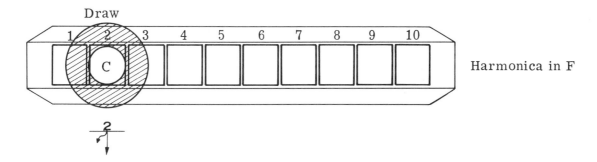

Harmonica in F

FILLS: added notes that are optional tones to be played at the end of phrases or breaks in the music. They can be added to the melody or just used as fill between the vocals.

Cross-harp can play these added notes:

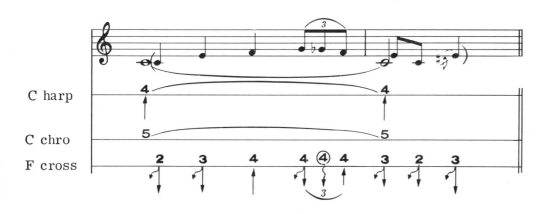

FOR FURTHER INFORMATION about cross-harp refer to: <u>BLUES HARP for Diatonic and Chromatic Harmonica</u> by Phil Duncan

GENERAL INFORMATION

1.   BLOW   DRAW

2. Top arrow is the rule:

3. Length of arrow is for duration of sound:

4. Tied notes: DO NOT REPEAT the second tone, but combine both for a longer duration.

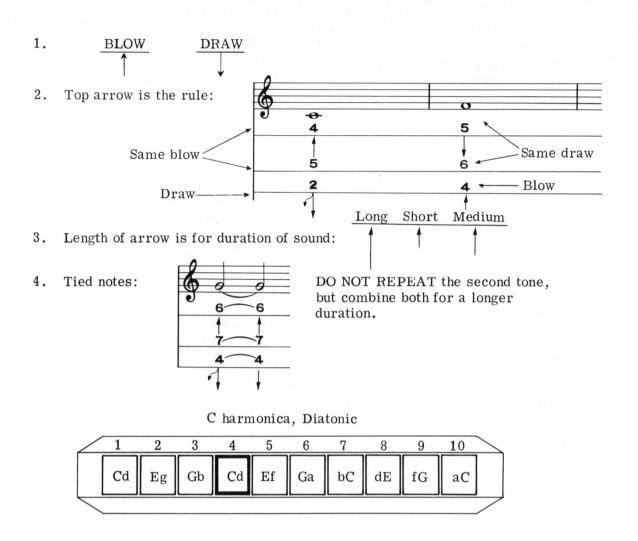

C harmonica, Diatonic

1	2	3	4	5	6	7	8	9	10
Cd	Eg	Gb	Cd	Ef	Ga	bC	dE	fG	aC

F cross - Harp

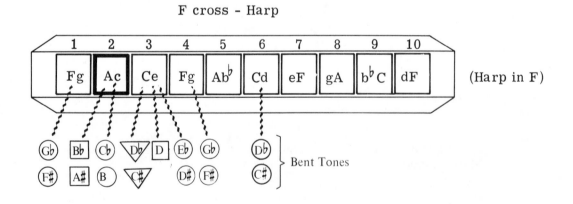

(Harp in F)

C harmonica, Chromatic

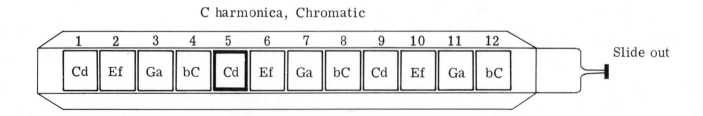

Slide out

1	2	3	4	5	6	7	8	9	10	11	12
Cd	Ef	Ga	bC	Cd	Ef	Ga	bC	Cd	Ef	Ga	bC

ALL THE GOOD TIMES ARE PAST AND GONE

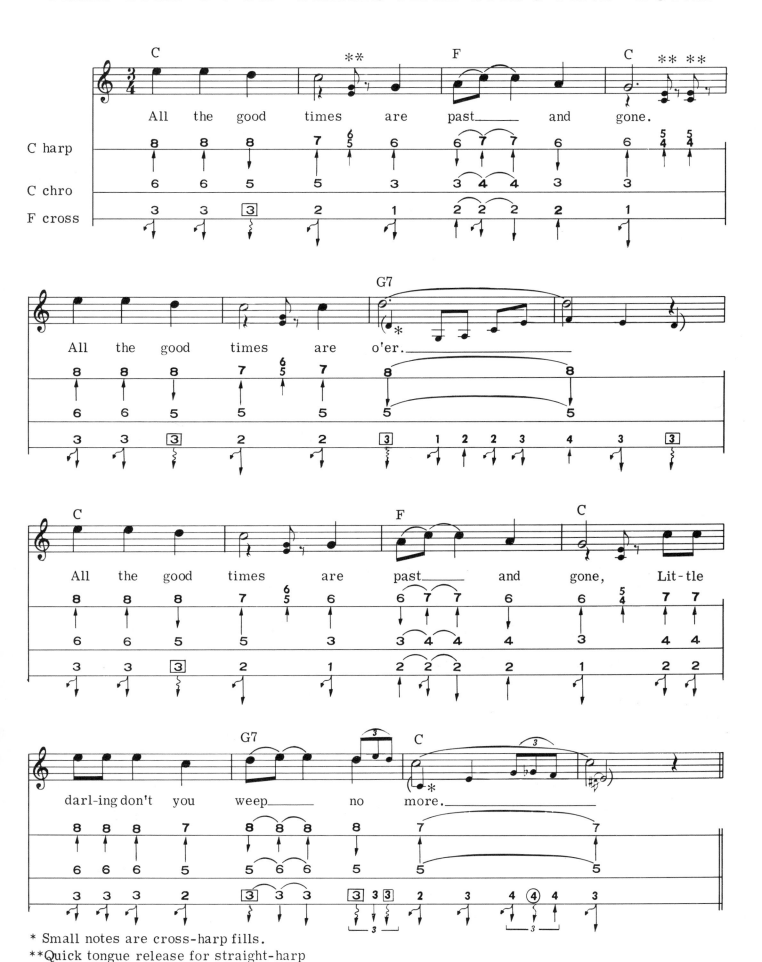

* Small notes are cross-harp fills.
**Quick tongue release for straight-harp

ARKANSAS TRAVELER

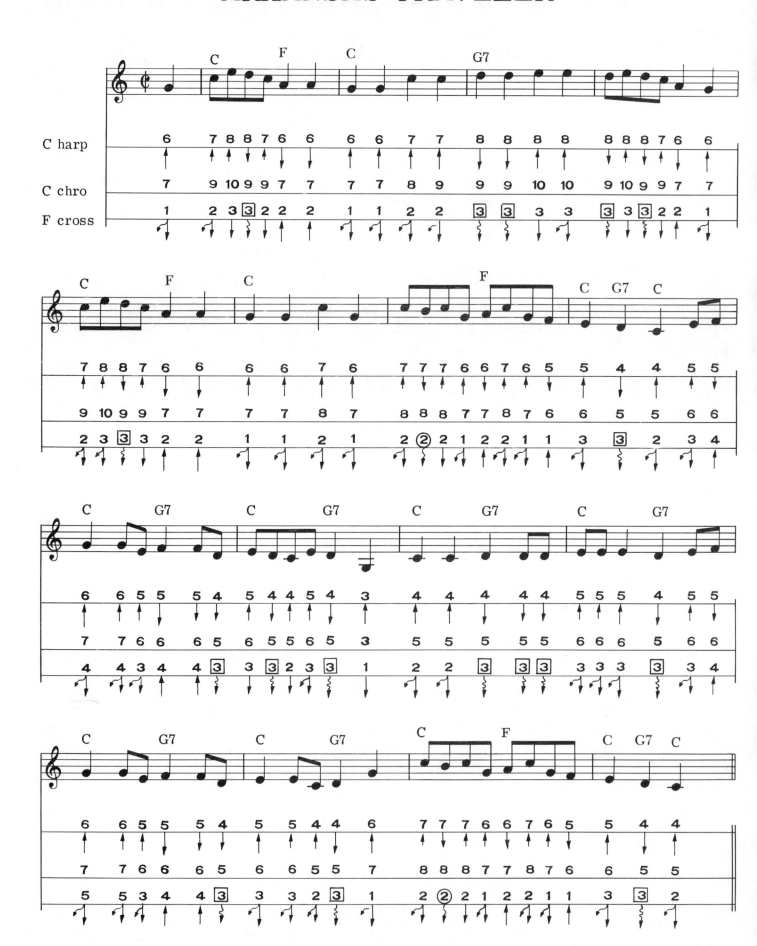

BANKS OF THE OHIO

BIG ROCK CANDY MOUNTAIN

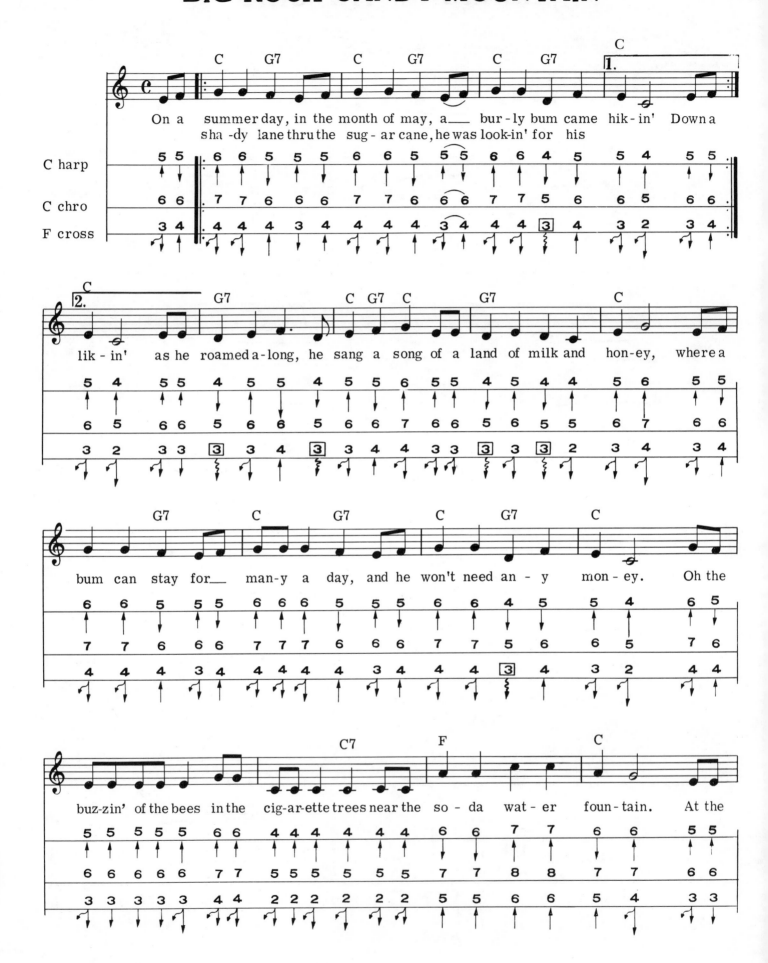

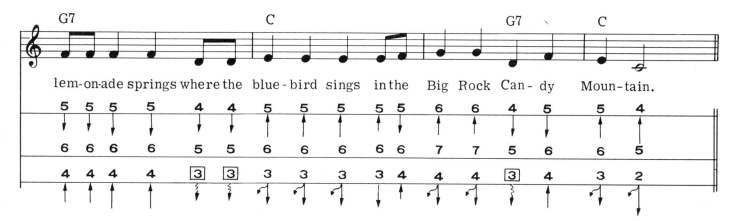

CRIPPLE CREEK

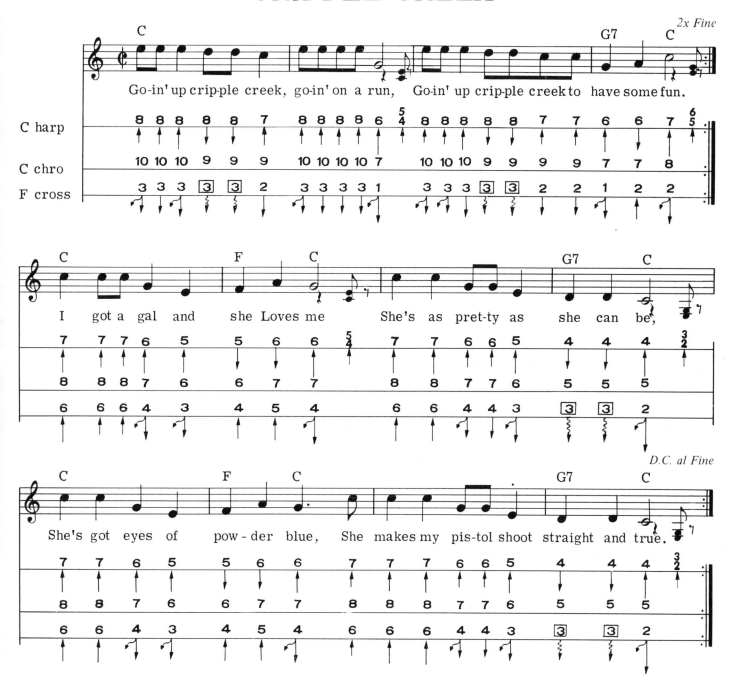

BILE 'DEM CABBAGE DOWN

CARELESS LOVE

* slowly move to pitch.

CIDER THROUGH A STRAW

CINDY

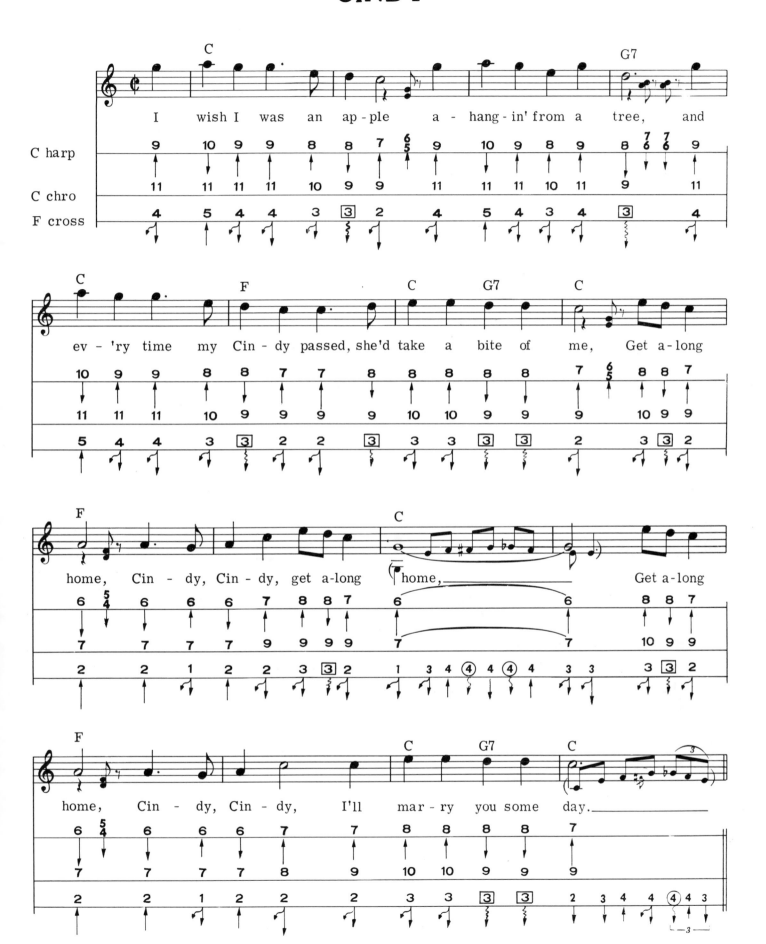

CRAWDAD SONG

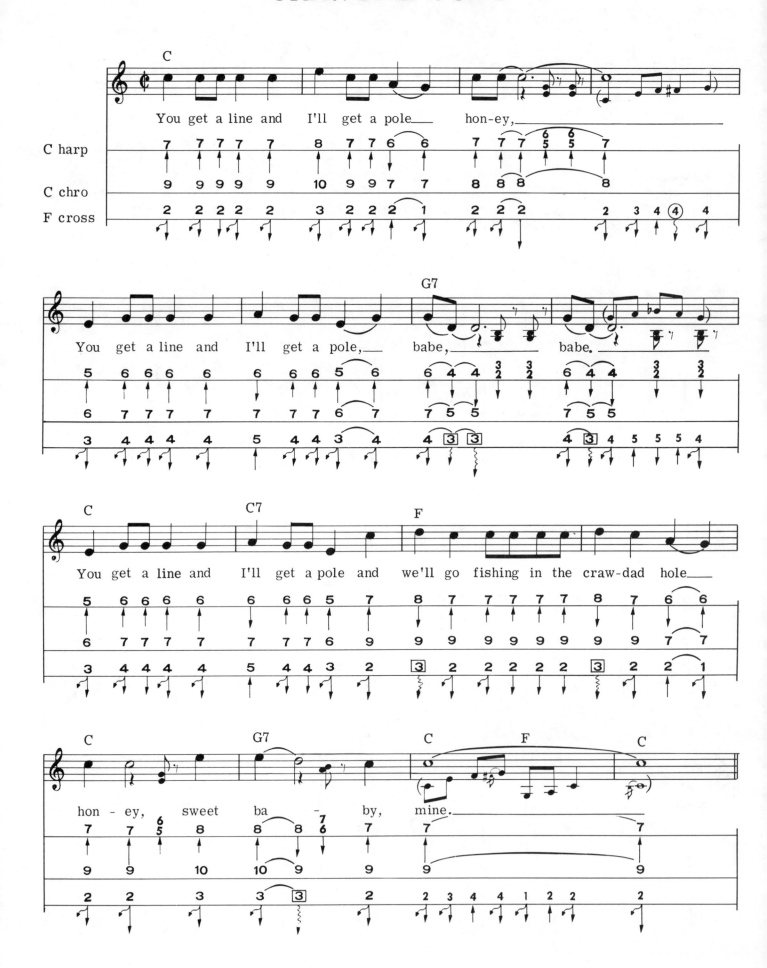

EAST VIRGINIA

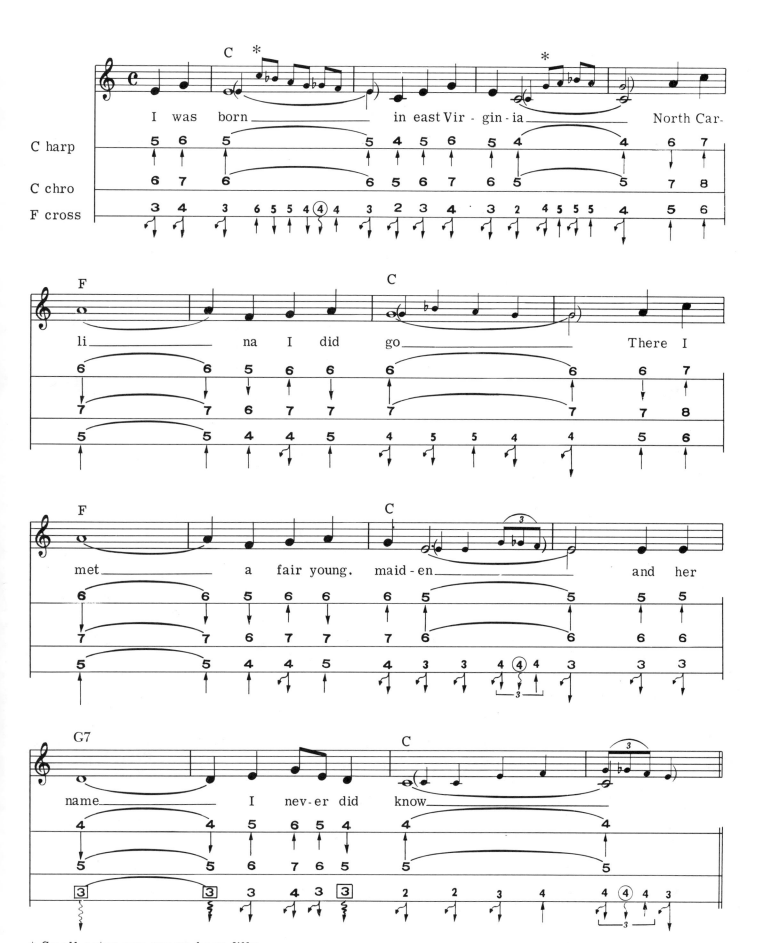

* Small notes are cross-harp fills.

FOGGY MOUNTAIN TOP

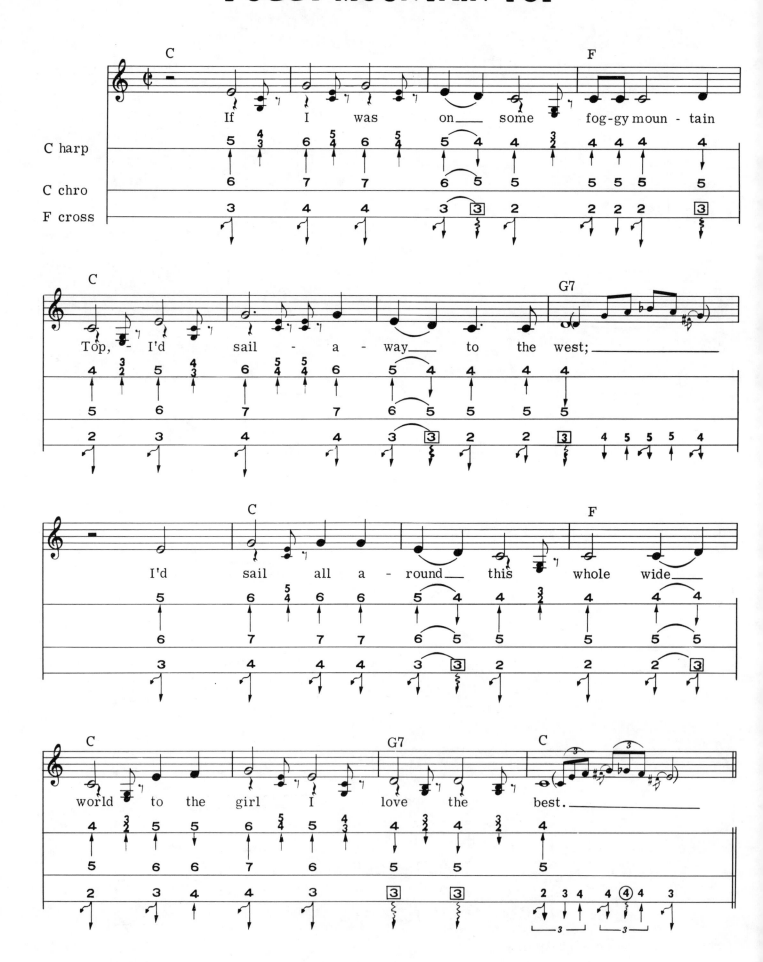

GOOBER PEAS

HAND ME DOWN MY WALKING CAME

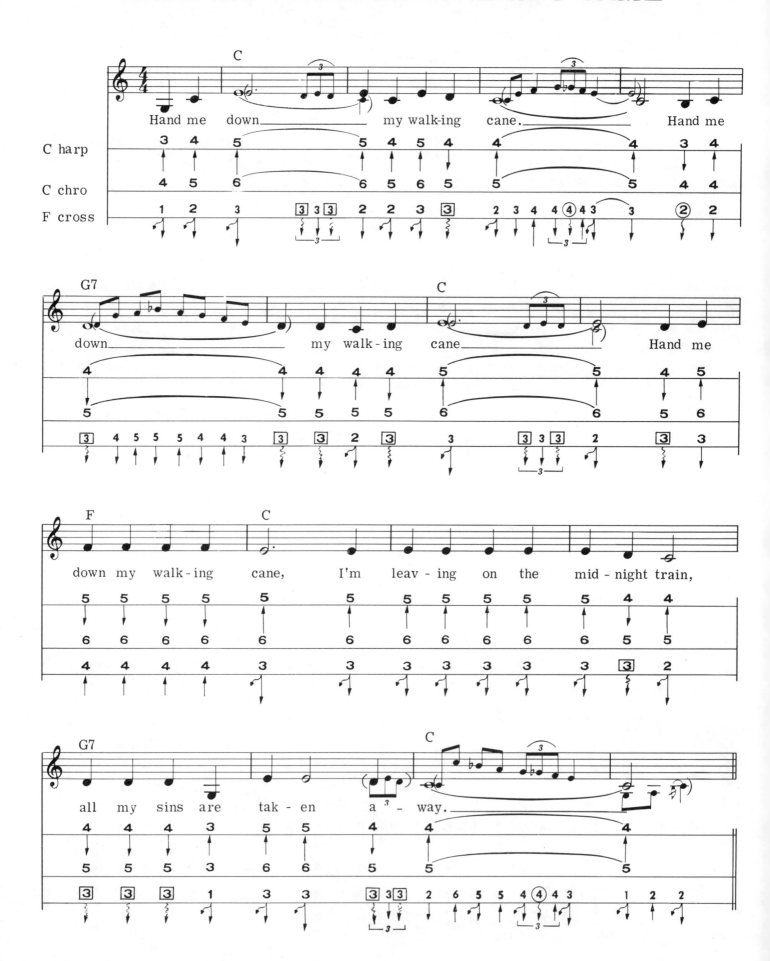

HARD, AIN'T IT HARD

I AM A PILGRIM

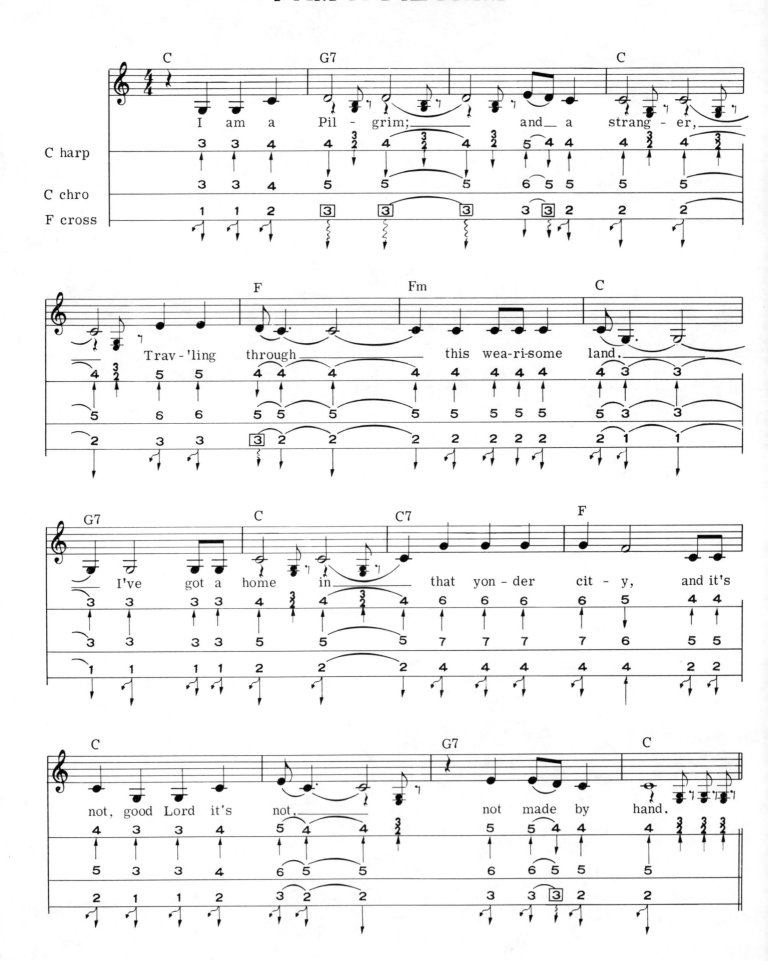

I WISH I WAS SINGLE AGAIN

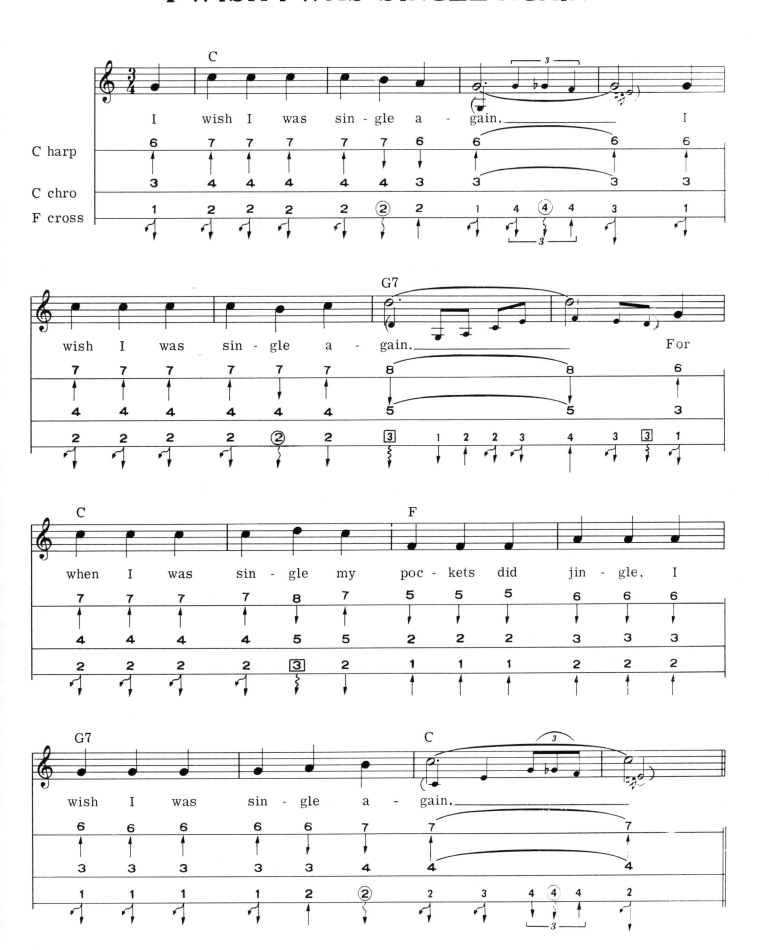

JOHN HARDY

* Needs a flatted 7th, C harp will be used in cross-position.

JOHN HENRY

JESSE JAMES
(BALLAD)

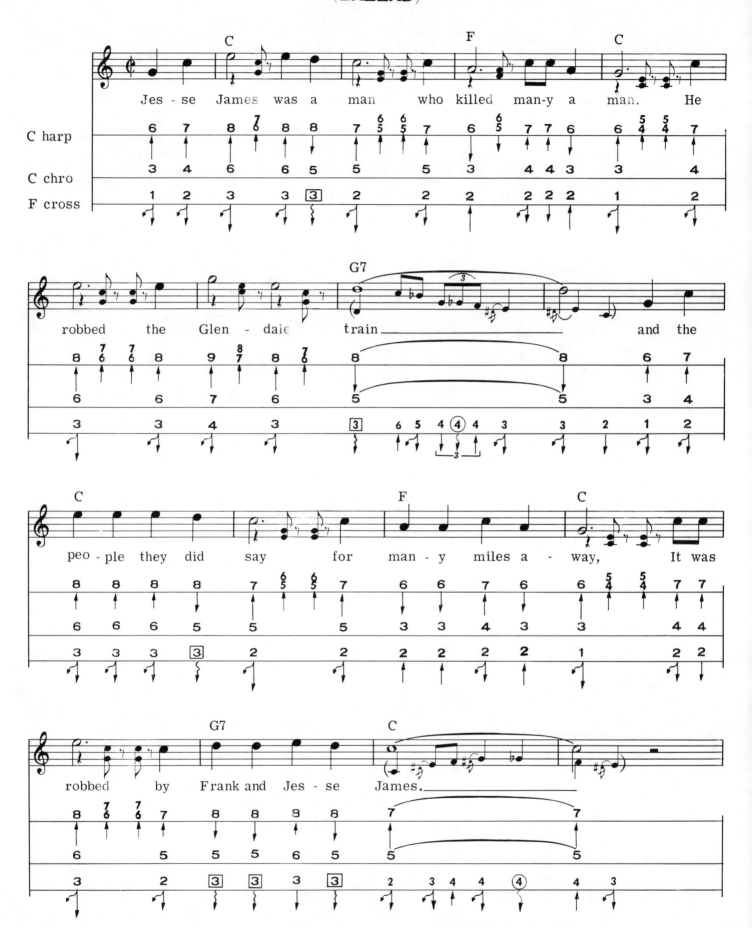

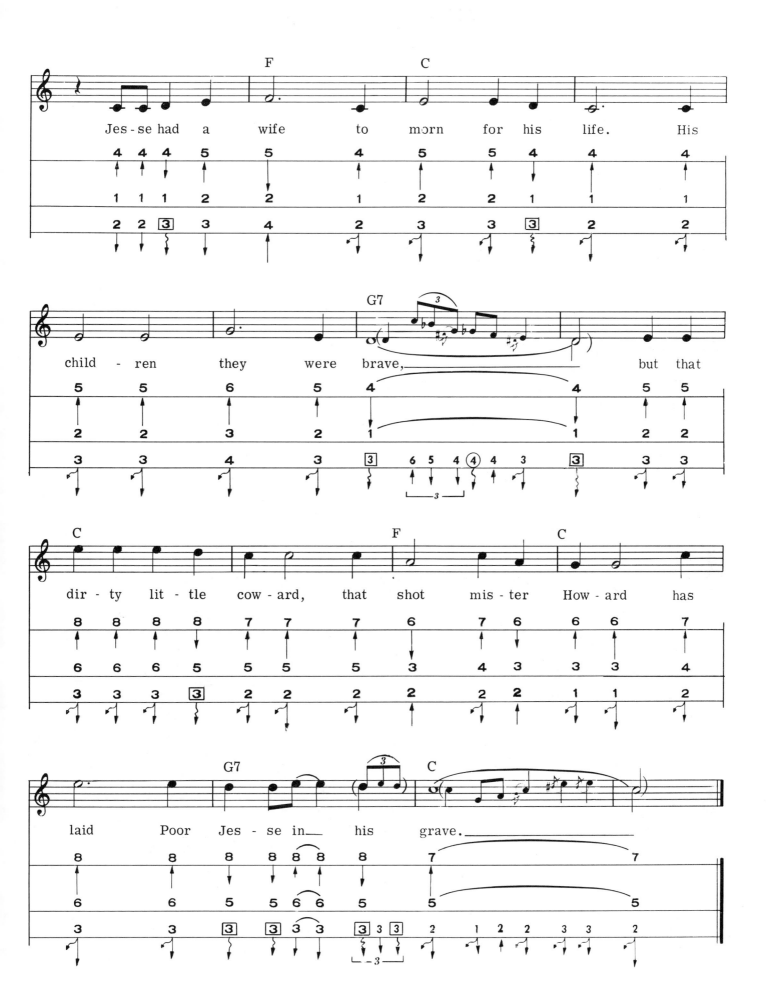

LITTLE MAGGIE

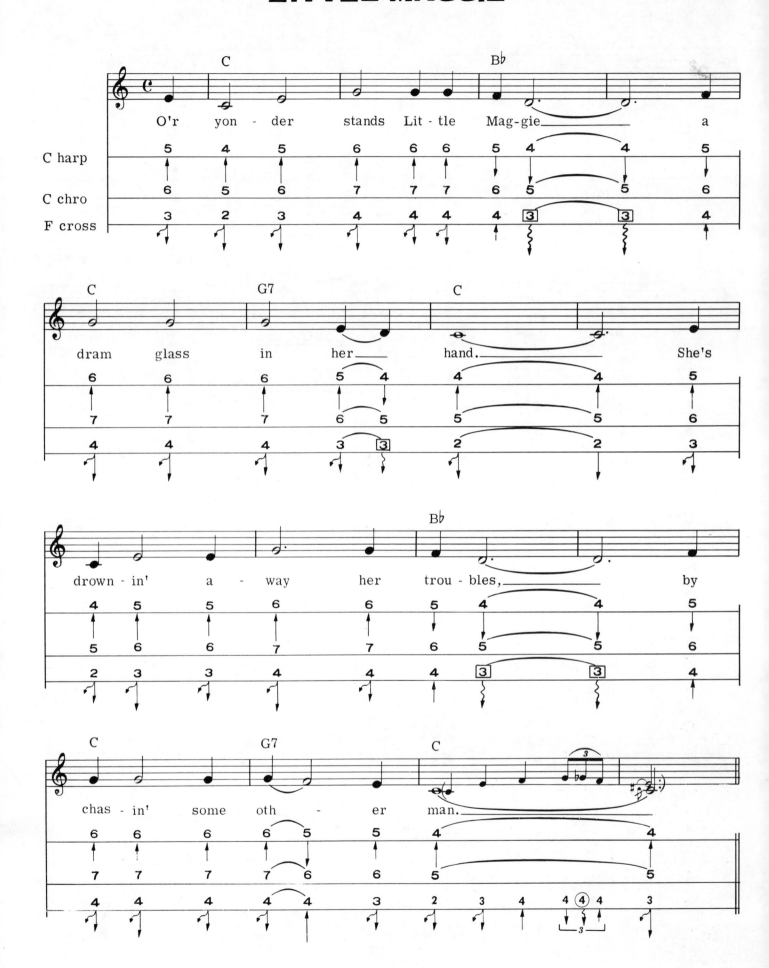

LONESOME ROAD BLUES

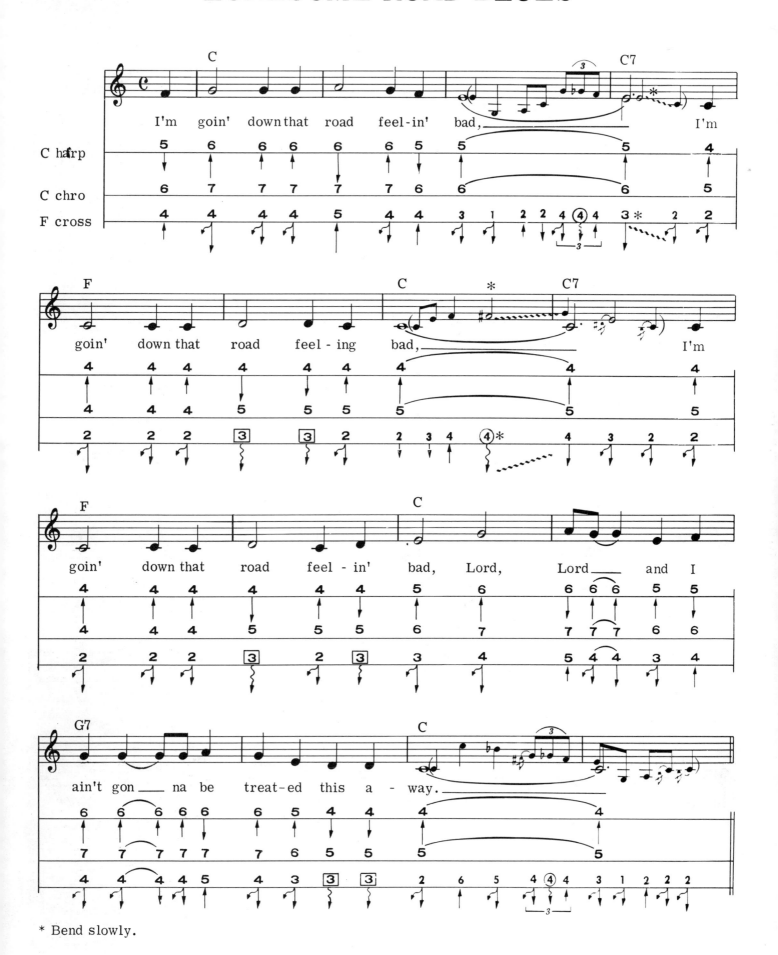

* Bend slowly.

LONESOME VALLEY

LONG JOURNEY HOME

LORD, I'M COMING HOME

MAMA DON'T 'LOW

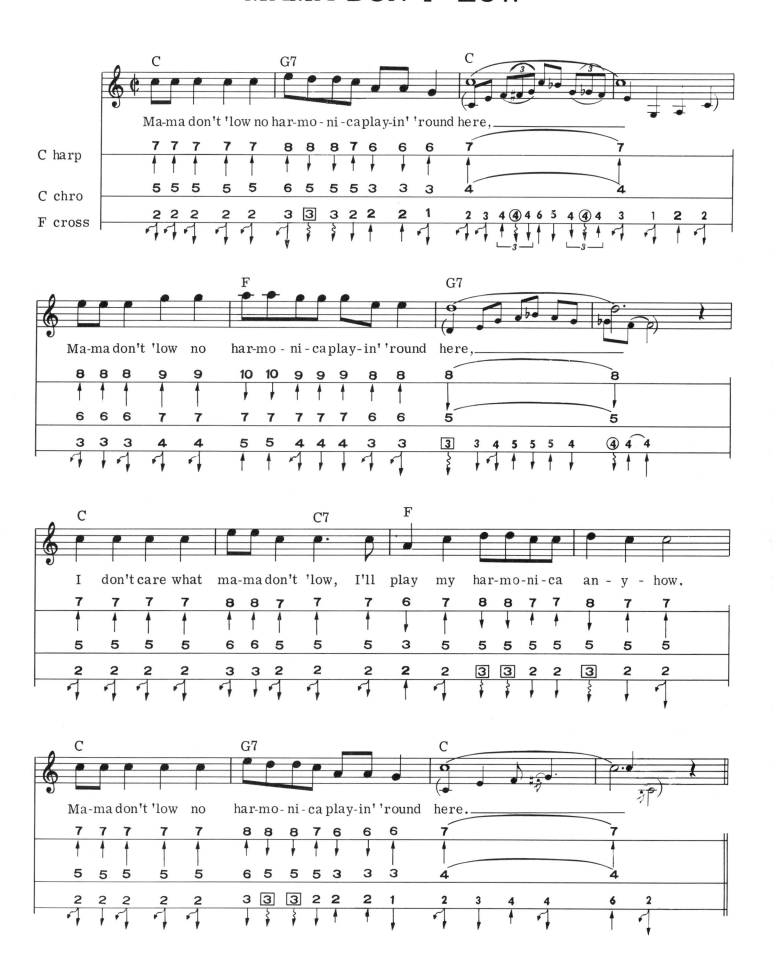

MIDNIGHT SPECIAL

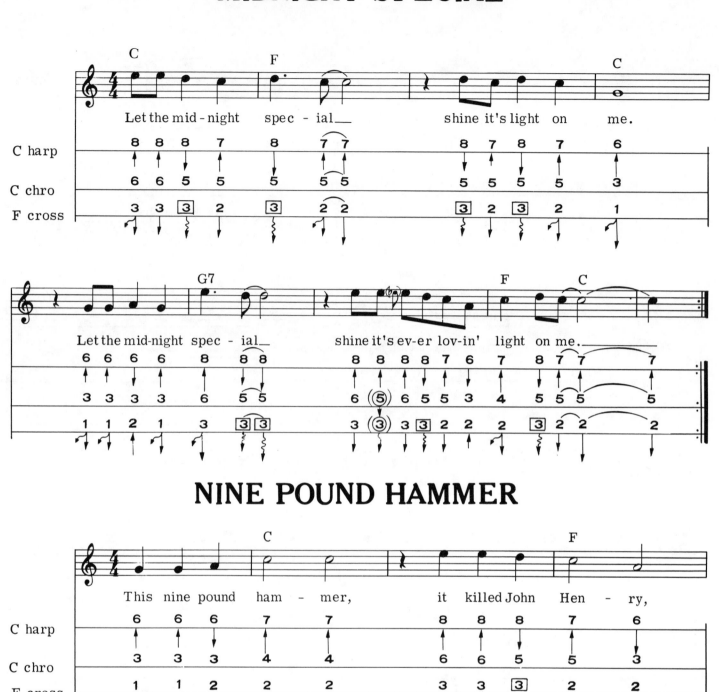

NINE POUND HAMMER

MY HOME'S ACROSS THE SMOKEY MOUNTAINS

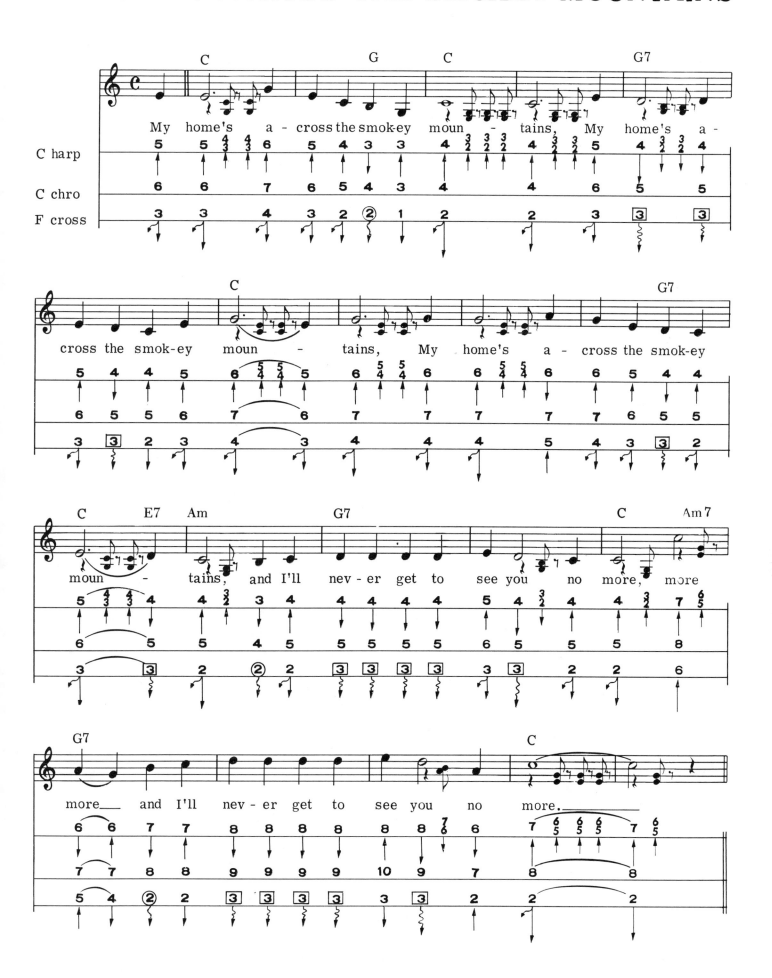

NEW RIVER TRAIN

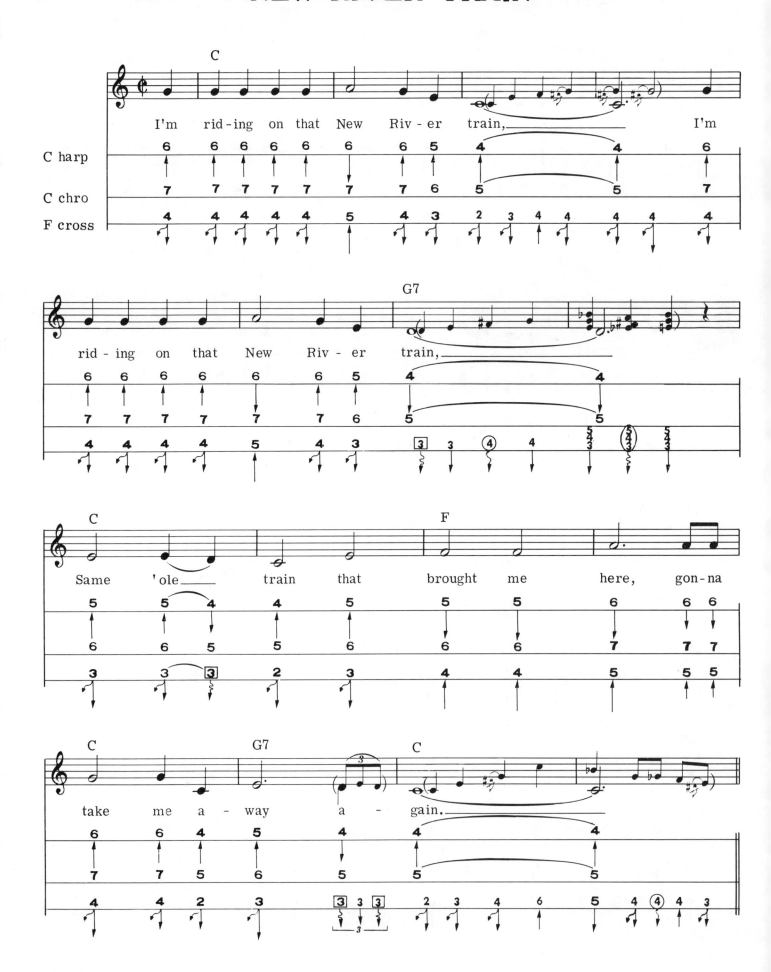

OH, MARY, DON'T YOU WEEP

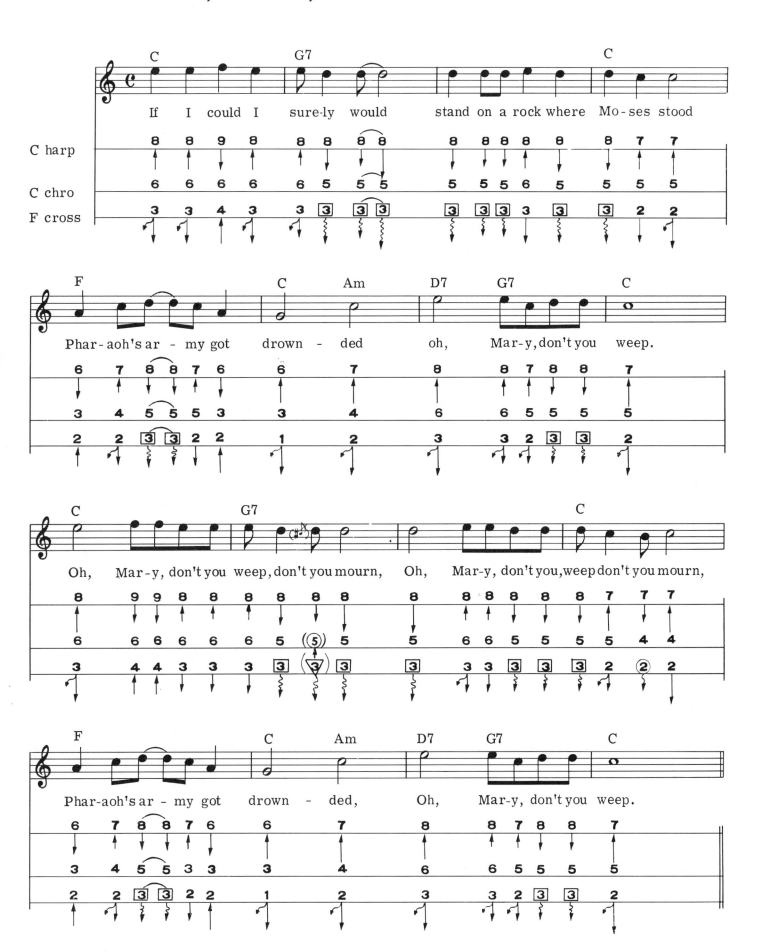

OLD JOE CLARK

* Old Joe Clack needs a flatted 7th (F♮) C harp will be used in cross position.

PRECIOUS MEMORIES

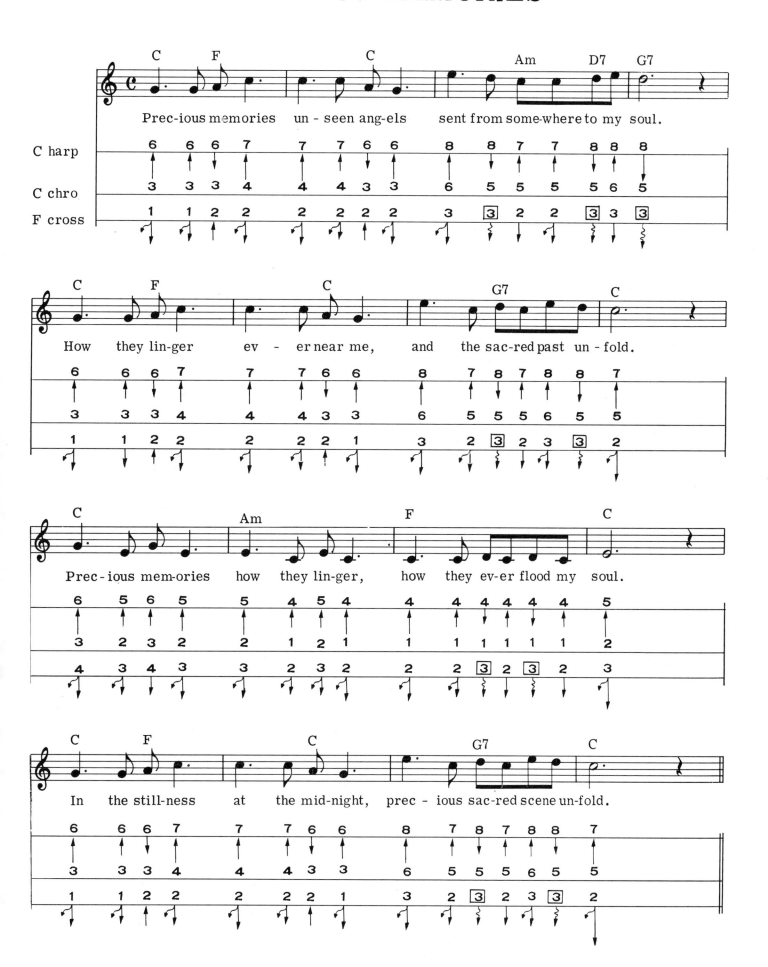

RAISE A RUCKUS TONIGHT

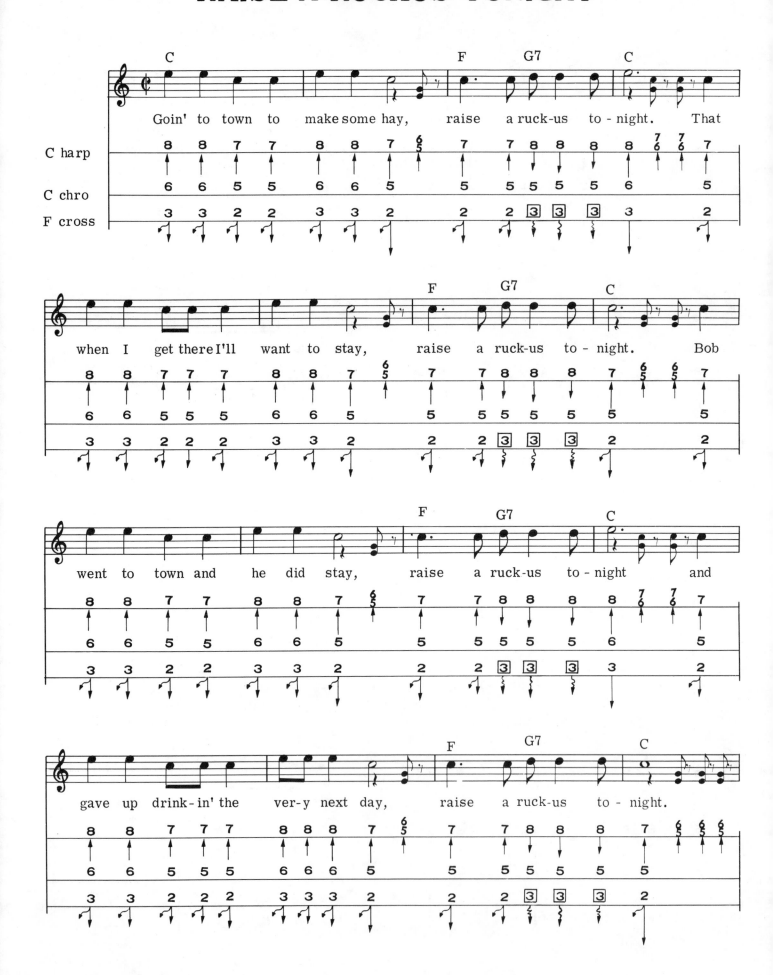

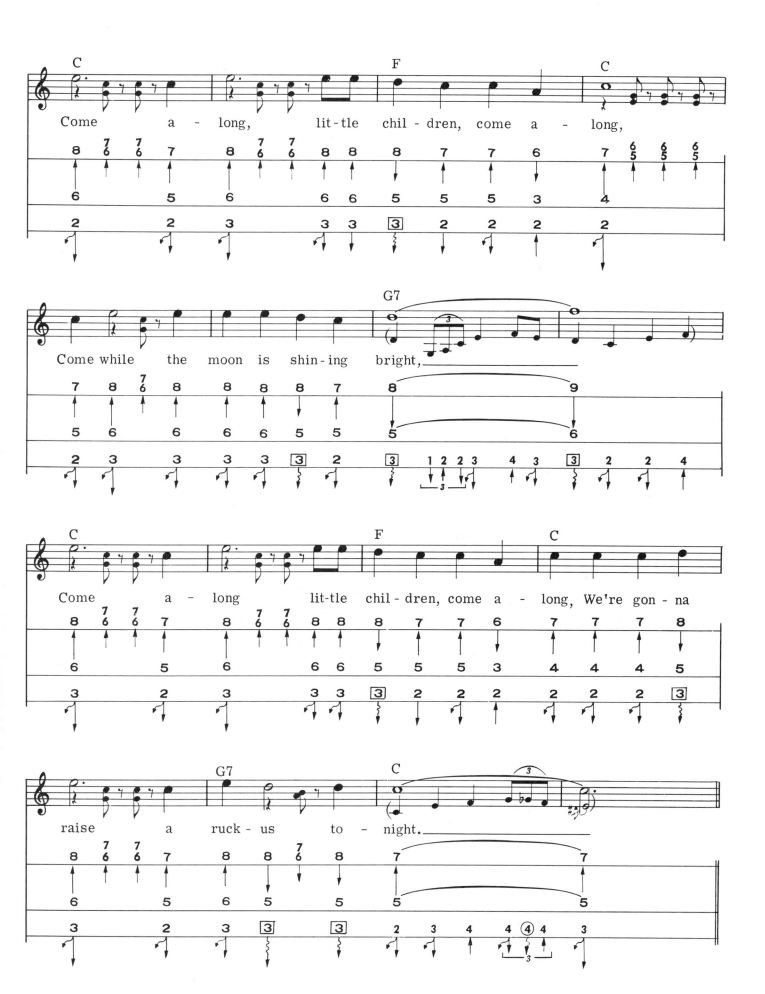

41

RAILROAD BILL

RED RIVER VALLEY

ROLL IN MY SWEET BABY'S ARMS

ROLL ON BUDDY

SALLY GOODIN'

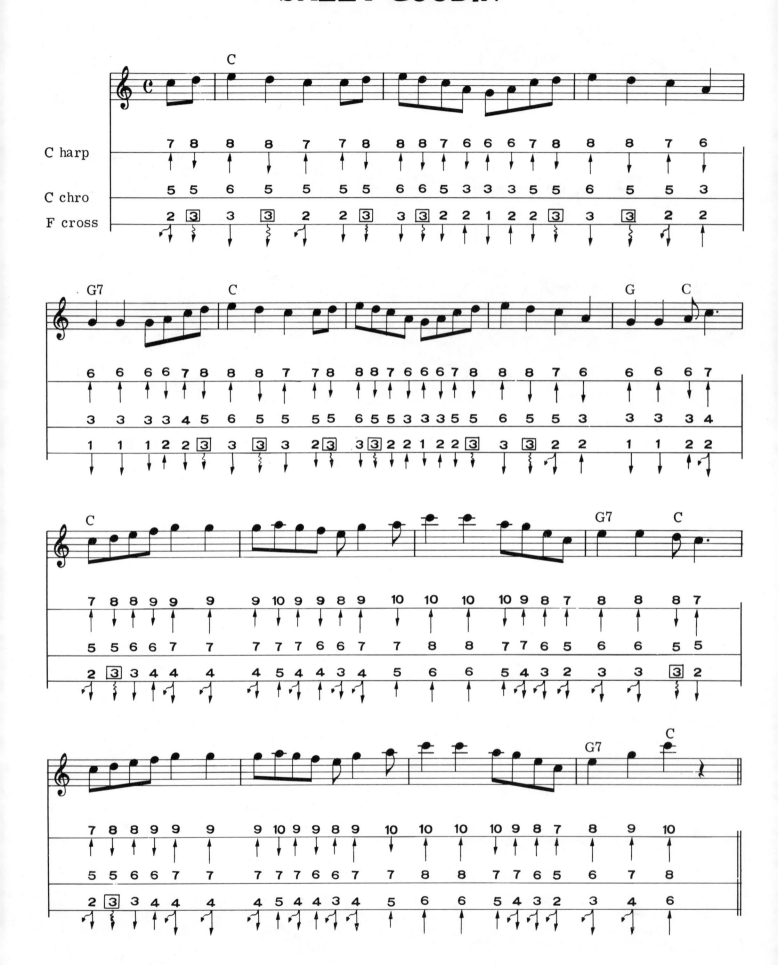

SOLDIER'S JOY

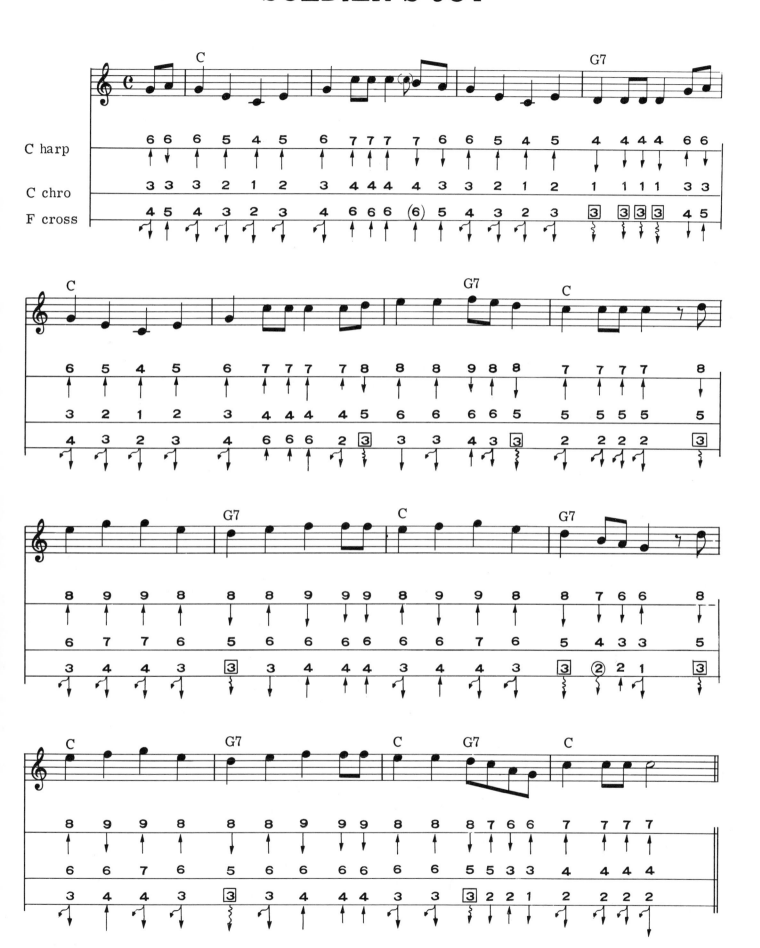

SOURWOOD MOUNTAIN

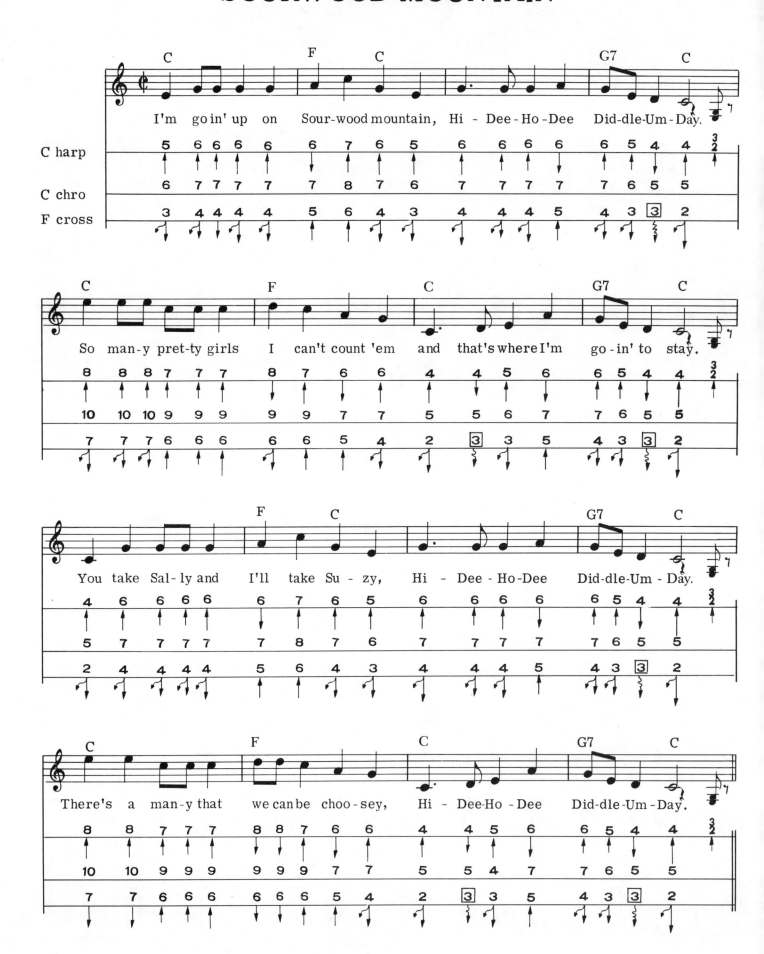

SWEET BY AND BY

THE FOGGY, FOGGY DEW

THE ROVING GAMBLER

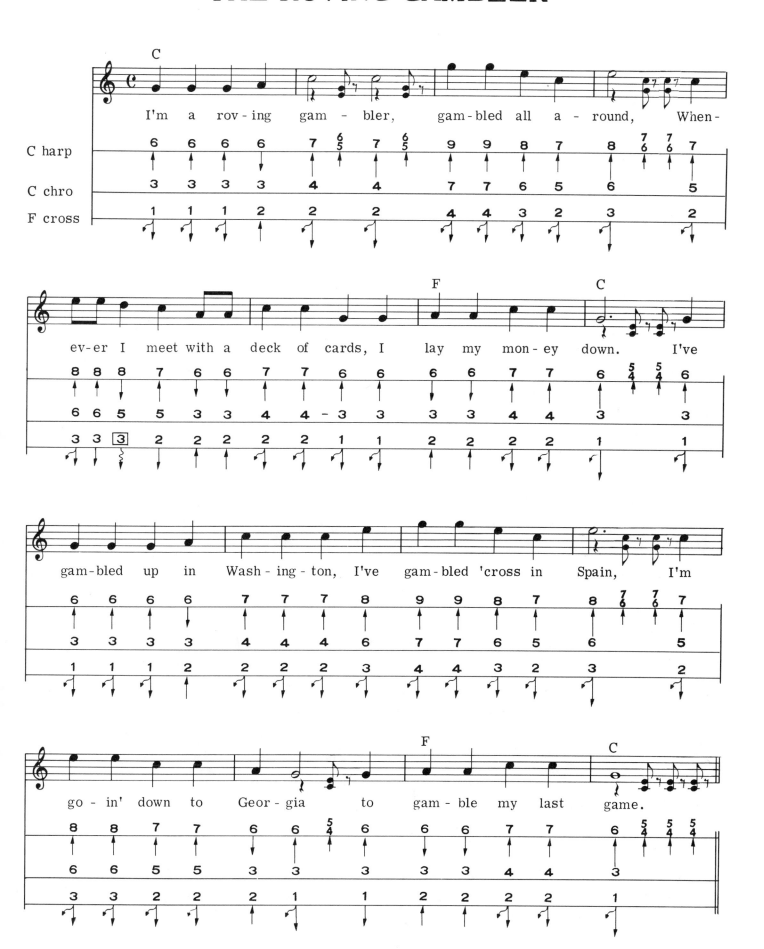

THIS TRAIN

TURKEY IN THE STRAW

Oh as I was a go-ing down a dus-ty, dus-ty road, with a team of hor-ses and a hea-vy load, It was

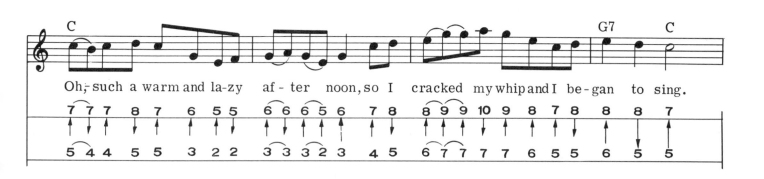

Oh, such a warm and la-zy af - ter noon, so I cracked my whip and I be-gan to sing.

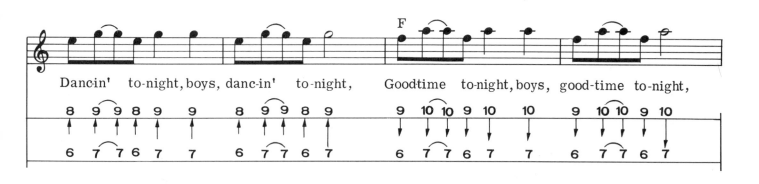

Dancin' to-night, boys, danc-in' to-night, Goodtime to-night, boys, good-time to-night,

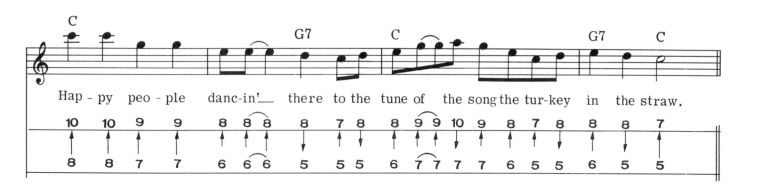

Hap - py peo - ple danc-in' there to the tune of the song the tur-key in the straw.

WABASH CANNON BALL

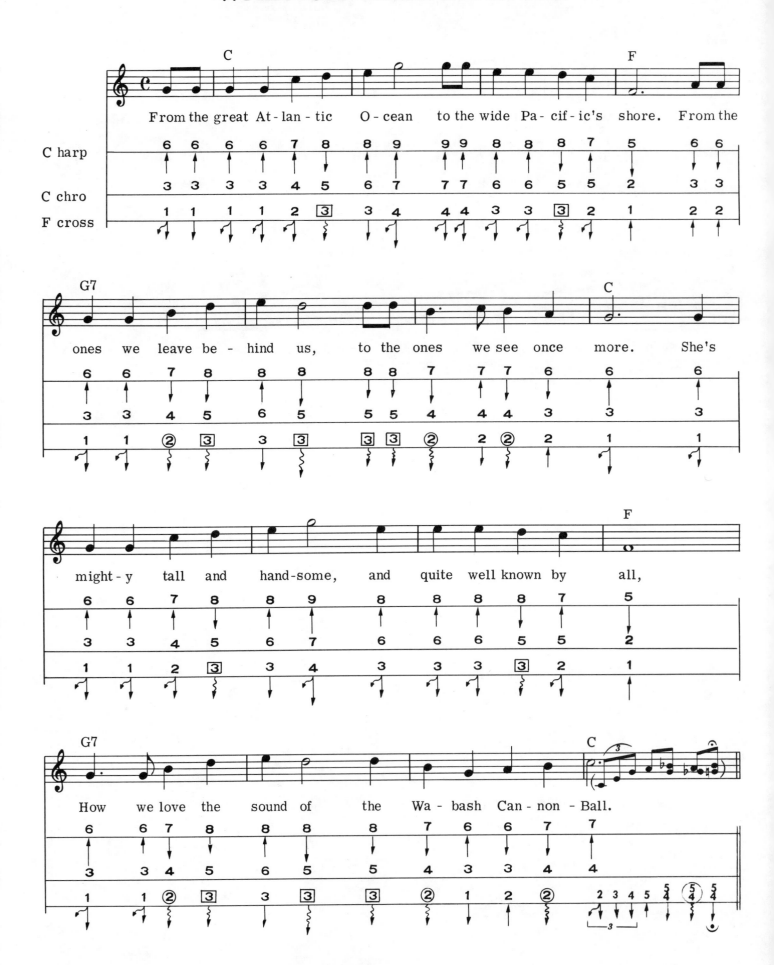

WILDWOOD FLOWER

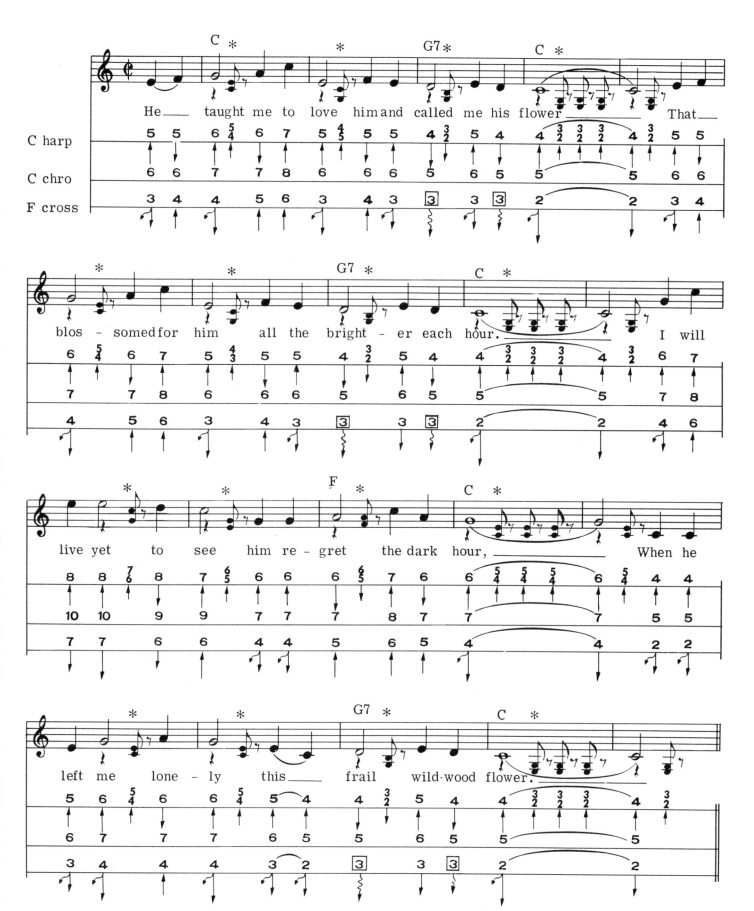

* Tongue quick release, diatonic only.

WORRIED MAN BLUES